EGMONT

We bring stories to life

First published in Great Britain in 1997 by Egmont UK Limited,
The Yellow Building, 1 Nicholas Road, London W11 4AN
This new edition first published in 2013
© 2013 Disney Enterprises, Inc
Based on the Winnie-the-Pooh works by A.A.Milne and E.H.Shepard

1 3 5 7 9 10 8 6 4 2
ISBN 978 1 4052 6652 9
Printed in Malaysia

54551/1

Winnie-the-Pooh
Baby Days

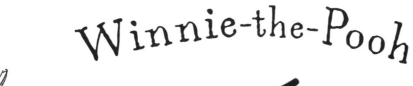

With texts by A.A.Milne

Illustrations by E.H.Shepard

Contents

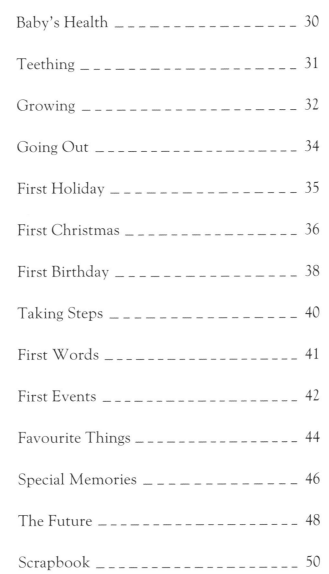

Waiting for Baby

Scan

Prenatal scan   Date _ _ _ _ _ _ _ _ _ _ _ _ _ _

Date baby due

_ _ _ _ _ _ _ _ _ _ _ _ _ _ _ _

Choice of names for baby

_ _

_ _

_ _

_ _

_ _

Mother's name

_ _

Father's name

_ _

How Mother and Father met

_ _

_ _

_ _

Now it happened that Kanga had felt rather motherly that morning, and Wanting to Count Things – like Roo's vests, and how many pieces of soap there were left, and the two clean spots in Tigger's feeder; so she sent them out with a packet of watercress sandwiches and a packet of extract-of-malt sandwiches for Tigger.

Feelings about having a baby

_____

_____

_____

_____

_____

When I first heard his name, I said, just as
you are going to say, "But I thought he was a boy?"
"So did I," said Christopher Robin.
"Then you can't call him Winnie?"
"I don't."
"But you said –"
"He's Winnie-ther-Pooh.
Don't you know what 'ther' means?"

Photograph

Mother/Father

9

Baby's Birth

	day	month	year
Baby was born on	_ _ _ _ _ _ _ _	_ _ _ _ _ _ _ _	_ _ _ _ _ _ _ _

Time of birth

_ _

Place of birth

_ _

Who was present at the birth

_ _

"When you wake up in the morning, Pooh," said Piglet at last, "what's the first thing you say to yourself?"
"What's for breakfast?" said Pooh.
"What do you say, Piglet?"
"I say, I wonder what's going to happen exciting today?" said Piglet.
Pooh nodded thoughtfully.
"It's the same thing," he said.

Weight at birth

_ _

Length at birth

_ _

Colour of eyes

_ _

Colour of hair

_ _

Name of midwife

_ _

Name of doctor

_ _

Photograph

Very first photograph of baby

Description of the birth

_ _

_ _

_ _

_ _

_ _

_ _

_ _

Things to Remember

Identity tag

Handprint

Footprint

"I think —" began Piglet nervously.
"Don't," said Eeyore.
"I think Violets are rather nice,"
said Piglet. And he laid his bunch in
front of Eeyore and scampered off.

Pressed flowers

Visitors

_ _ _ _ _ _ _ _ _ _ _ _ _ _ _ _

_ _ _ _ _ _ _ _ _ _ _ _ _ _ _ _

_ _ _ _ _ _ _ _ _ _ _ _ _ _ _ _

_ _ _ _ _ _ _ _ _ _ _ _ _ _ _ _

_ _ _ _ _ _ _ _ _ _ _ _ _ _ _ _

Who sent flowers

_ _ _ _ _ _ _ _ _ _ _ _ _ _ _ _

_ _ _ _ _ _ _ _ _ _ _ _ _ _ _ _

_ _ _ _ _ _ _ _ _ _ _ _ _ _ _ _

_ _ _ _ _ _ _ _ _ _ _ _ _ _ _ _

_ _ _ _ _ _ _ _ _ _ _ _ _ _ _ _

Cards and gifts from   Date

_ _ _ _ _ _ _ _ _ _ _ _ _ _ _ _   _ _ _ _ _ _ _ _

_ _ _ _ _ _ _ _ _ _ _ _ _ _ _ _   _ _ _ _ _ _ _ _

_ _ _ _ _ _ _ _ _ _ _ _ _ _ _ _   _ _ _ _ _ _ _ _

_ _ _ _ _ _ _ _ _ _ _ _ _ _ _ _   _ _ _ _ _ _ _ _

_ _ _ _ _ _ _ _ _ _ _ _ _ _ _ _   _ _ _ _ _ _ _ _

Baby's Arrival

Newspaper cuttings
and cards

Birth Announcements

Baby's First Day

Distinctive features

_ _

_ _

Sign of the Zodiac

_ _

Weather on this day

_ _

_ _

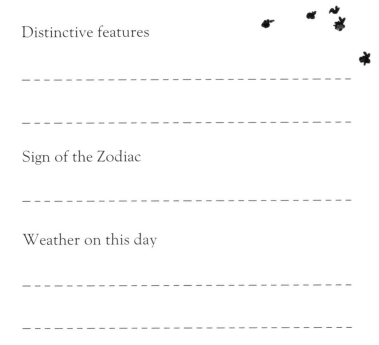

No one can tell me,
Nobody knows,
Where the wind comes from,
Where the wind goes.

It's flying from somewhere
As fast as it can,
I couldn't keep up with it,
Not if I ran.

But if I stopped holding
The string of my kite,
It would blow with the wind
For a day and a night.

And then when I found it,
Wherever it blew,
I should know that the wind
Had been going there too.

So then I could tell them
Where the wind goes . . .
But where the wind comes from
Nobody knows.

On This Day

Famous events in history which happened on this date

‗ ‗ ‗ ‗ ‗ ‗ ‗ ‗ ‗ ‗ ‗ ‗ ‗ ‗ ‗ ‗ ‗ ‗

‗ ‗ ‗ ‗ ‗ ‗ ‗ ‗ ‗ ‗ ‗ ‗ ‗ ‗ ‗ ‗ ‗ ‗

‗ ‗ ‗ ‗ ‗ ‗ ‗ ‗ ‗ ‗ ‗ ‗ ‗ ‗ ‗ ‗ ‗ ‗

‗ ‗ ‗ ‗ ‗ ‗ ‗ ‗ ‗ ‗ ‗ ‗ ‗ ‗ ‗ ‗ ‗ ‗

‗ ‗ ‗ ‗ ‗ ‗ ‗ ‗ ‗ ‗ ‗ ‗ ‗ ‗ ‗ ‗ ‗ ‗

Famous people born on this day

‗ ‗ ‗ ‗ ‗ ‗ ‗ ‗ ‗ ‗ ‗ ‗ ‗ ‗ ‗ ‗

‗ ‗ ‗ ‗ ‗ ‗ ‗ ‗ ‗ ‗ ‗ ‗ ‗ ‗ ‗ ‗

‗ ‗ ‗ ‗ ‗ ‗ ‗ ‗ ‗ ‗ ‗ ‗ ‗ ‗ ‗ ‗

‗ ‗ ‗ ‗ ‗ ‗ ‗ ‗ ‗ ‗ ‗ ‗ ‗ ‗ ‗ ‗

No.1 in the music charts

‗ ‗ ‗ ‗ ‗ ‗ ‗ ‗ ‗ ‗ ‗ ‗ ‗ ‗ ‗ ‗

"Are you," he said, "by any chance
His Majesty the King of France?"
The other answered, "I am that,"
Bowed stiffly, and removed his hat;
Then said, "Excuse me," with an air,
"But is it Mr Edward Bear?"

And Teddy, bending very low,
Replied politely, "Even so!"

Front page of the newspaper today

Coming Home

Baby came home on

_____

Address of family home

_____

_____

Who was there to welcome baby?

_____

_____

_____

_____

On the first night home baby fell asleep at

_____ am/pm

_____ am/pm

Baby woke at

_____ am/pm

_____ am/pm

Photograph

Baby's first night at home

Settling Down

Baby's feeding times

_ _

_ _

Breast or bottle?

_ _

Sleeping times

_ _

Wakeful times

_ _

Favourite sleeping position

_ _

Then Tigger looked up at the ceiling, and closed his eyes, and his tongue went round and round his chops, in case he had left any outside, and a peaceful smile came over his face as he said, "So that's what Tiggers like!"

Mother's feelings

_ _

_ _

_ _

Father's feelings

_ _

_ _

_ _

Naming Baby

Pooh

Now this bear's name is Winnie, which shows what a good name for bears it is, but the funny thing is that we can't remember whether Winnie is called after Pooh, or Pooh after Winnie. We did know once, but we have forgotten.

Baby's name

— —

Date of Christening or Name Day celebrations

— —

Baby wore

— —

Godparents

— —

— —

— —

Photograph

Baby's Day

Piglet

Baby's name means

Name was chosen by

Reason for choosing name

Gifts received

Photograph

The Celebrations

Family Tree

Family photograph

Next to his house was a piece of broken board which had:
"TRESPASSERS W" on it. When Christopher Robin asked
the Piglet what it meant, he said it was his grandfather's
name, and had been in the family for a long time.

Mother's side

Father's side

Great Grandmother

_ _

Great Grandfather

_ _

Grandmother

_ _

Grandfather

_ _

Baby's Mother

_ _

Great Grandmother

_ _

Great Grandfather

_ _

Grandmother

_ _

Grandfather

_ _

Baby's Father

_ _

Baby's Sisters

Baby's Brothers

_ _ _ _ _ _ _ _ _ _ _ _ _ _ _ _ _

_ _ _ _ _ _ _ _ _ _ _ _ _ _ _ _ _

_ _ _ _ _ _ _ _ _ _ _ _ _ _ _ _ _

_ _ _ _ _ _ _ _ _ _ _ _ _ _ _ _ _

_ _ _ _ _ _ _ _ _ _ _ _ _ _ _ _ _

_ _ _ _ _ _ _ _ _ _ _ _ _ _ _ _ _

Baby's Progress

Photograph

Date _

Wakes up at

_ _ _ _ _ _ _ _ _ _ _ _ _ _ _ _ _ _

Bathtime

_ _ _ _ _ _ _ _ _ _ _ _ _ _ _ _ _ _

Mealtimes

_ _ _ _ _ _ _ _ _ _ _ _ _ _ _ _ _ _

_ _ _ _ _ _ _ _ _ _ _ _ _ _ _ _ _ _

_ _ _ _ _ _ _ _ _ _ _ _ _ _ _ _ _ _

Goes to sleep at

_ _ _ _ _ _ _ _ _ _ _ _ _ _ _ _ _ _

*Sometimes Winnie-the-Pooh likes a game of
some sort when he comes downstairs,
and sometimes he likes to sit quietly in front
of the fire and listen to a story . . .*

24

How baby has changed

_____

_____

_____

_____

_____

Favourite activities

_____

_____

_____

_____

_____

Describe baby's first weeks

_____

_____

_____

_____

_____

Bathtime

Does baby like bathtime?

_____

Favourite bath toys

_____

Favourite bath games

_____

First bath at home

_____

First time in the big bath

_____

Photograph

Baby's bathtime

Bedtime

Sleeping times

_____

_____

First slept through the night

_____

Moved to a cot

_____

_____

Favourite bedtime toys

_____

_____

Favourite bedtime stories

_____

_____

Favourite lullabies

_____

_____

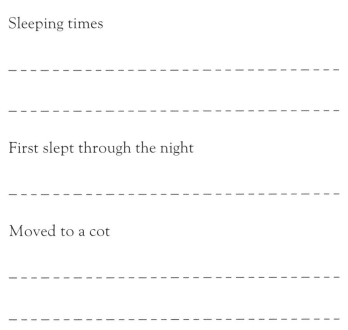

"Well," said Pooh, "it's the middle of the night, which is a good time for going to sleep. And tomorrow morning we'll have some honey for breakfast. Do Tiggers like honey?"
"They like everything," said Tigger cheerfully.

Mealtimes

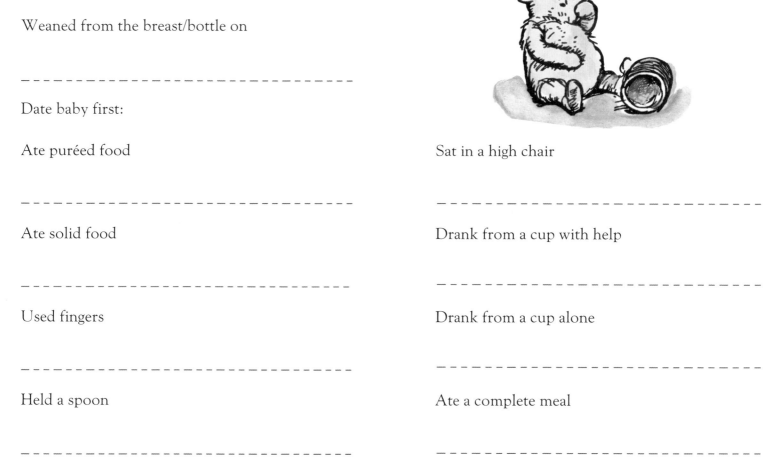

Weaned from the breast/bottle on

Date baby first:

Ate puréed food

Ate solid food

Used fingers

Held a spoon

Sat in a high chair

Drank from a cup with help

Drank from a cup alone

Ate a complete meal

*Pooh put the cloth back on the table, and he put a large
honey-pot on the cloth, and they sat down to breakfast.
And as soon as they sat down, Tigger took a large mouthful
of honey . . . and he looked up at the ceiling with his head
on one side, and made exploring noises with his tongue, and
considering noises, and what-have-we-got-here noises . . .
and then he said in a very decided voice:
"Tiggers don't like honey."*

Food liked

_____

Food disliked

_____

Photograph

Photograph

Baby eating

Favourite food

_____

_____

29

Baby's Health

Childhood illnesses   Date

__ __ __ __ __ __ __ __ __ __ __ __   __ __ __ __ __ __ __ __

__ __ __ __ __ __ __ __ __ __ __ __   __ __ __ __ __ __ __ __

__ __ __ __ __ __ __ __ __ __ __ __   __ __ __ __ __ __ __ __

Allergies

__ __ __ __ __ __ __ __ __ __ __ __ __ __ __

__ __ __ __ __ __ __ __ __ __ __ __ __ __ __

__ __ __ __ __ __ __ __ __ __ __ __ __ __ __

__ __ __ __ __ __ __ __ __ __ __ __ __ __ __

Eyesight test

__ __

Hearing test

__ __

Blood group

__ __

Local doctor

__ __

__ __

Telephone number

__ __

"I don't think Roo had better come," he said. "Not today."
"Why not?" said Roo, who wasn't supposed to be listening.
"Nasty cold today," said Rabbit, shaking his head. "And you were coughing this morning."
"How do you know?" asked Roo indignantly.
"Oh, Roo, you never told me," said Kanga reproachfully.
"It was a biscuit cough," said Roo, "not one you tell about."

Teething

A baby cuts 20 primary or milk teeth from about six months old to two years old. The appearance of the first tooth is a milestone in a baby's life, although it can cause a great deal of discomfort. Some babies find chewing on a teething ring soothes the gums and helps lessen the pain. These first milk teeth begin to be replaced with permanent teeth when the child is about six years old.

Date of first tooth

_ _

Date of second tooth

_ _

Date of third tooth

_ _

Date of fourth tooth

_ _

Date of fifth tooth

_ _

Date of sixth tooth

_ _

Date of seventh tooth

_ _

Date of eighth tooth

_ _

Date of ninth tooth

_ _

Date of tenth tooth

_ _

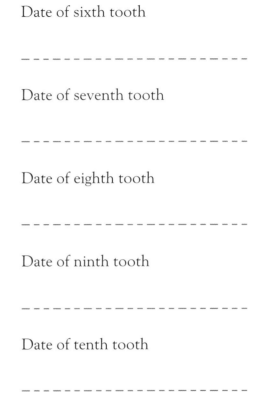

Binker isn't greedy, but he does like things to eat,
So I have to say to people when they're giving me a sweet,
"Oh, Binker wants a chocolate, so could you give me two?"
And then I eat it for him, 'cos his teeth are rather new.

Growing

Age	Weight	Length/Height
One month	– – – – – – – – – – – – –	– – – – – – – – – – – – –
Two months	– – – – – – – – – – – – –	– – – – – – – – – – – – –
Three months	– – – – – – – – – – – – –	– – – – – – – – – – – – –
Four months	– – – – – – – – – – – – –	– – – – – – – – – – – – –
Five months	– – – – – – – – – – – – –	– – – – – – – – – – – – –
Six months	– – – – – – – – – – – – –	– – – – – – – – – – – – –
Seven months	– – – – – – – – – – – – –	– – – – – – – – – – – – –
Eight months	– – – – – – – – – – – – –	– – – – – – – – – – – – –
Nine months	– – – – – – – – – – – – –	– – – – – – – – – – – – –
Ten months	– – – – – – – – – – – – –	– – – – – – – – – – – – –
Eleven months	– – – – – – – – – – – – –	– – – – – – – – – – – – –
Twelve months	– – – – – – – – – – – – –	– – – – – – – – – – – – –

What shall we do about poor little Tigger?
If he never eats nothing he'll never get bigger.
But whatever his weight in pounds, shillings and ounces,
He always seems bigger because of his bounces.

Photograph

Photograph

Baby at _ _ _ _ months

Baby at _ _ _ _ months

"He's quite big enough anyhow," said Piglet.
"He isn't really very big."
"Well he seems so."

Going Out

First outing in pram/push chair

_____

First outings made by:

Car   _____

Train   _____

Bus   _____

Photograph

Baby on an outing to _____

Special outings with:

Grandparents

_____

_____

Relatives

_____

_____

Friends

_____

_____

_____

First Holiday

First holiday

_ _

Travelled by

_ _

Where it was spent

_ _

Favourite activity

_ _

Favourite outings

_ _

_ _

"Christopher Robin and I are going for a Short Walk,"
he said, "not a Jostle. If he likes to bring Pooh and Piglet
with him, I shall be glad of their company, but one must
be able to Breathe."

Photograph

Baby on holiday in _ _ _ _ _ _ _ _ _ _ _ _ _ _ _

Favourite memories of the holiday

_ _

_ _

First Christmas

Photograph

Baby's first Christmas

The more it snows
(Tiddely pom),
The more it goes
(Tiddely pom),
The more it goes
(Tiddely pom)
On Snowing.
And nobody knows
(Tiddely pom),
How cold my toes
(Tiddely pom),
How cold my toes
(Tiddely pom),
Are growing.

Description of Christmas Day

_____

_____

Who it was spent with

_____

Where it was spent   _____

_____

Where Boxing Day was spent

Who it was spent with

Your present to baby

Stocking gifts

Description of Boxing Day

Gifts received   from

------------------   ------------------

------------------   ------------------

------------------   ------------------

------------------   ------------------

First Birthday

Date

_____

How it was celebrated

_____

_____

_____

Who was there

_____

_____

_____

Photograph

First birthday

Where it was spent

_____

Description of cake

- -

- -

What baby wore

- -

- -

Gifts received   from

- - - - - - - - - - - - -   - - - - - - - - - - - - -

- - - - - - - - - - - - -   - - - - - - - - - - - - -

Piglet had gone back to his own house to get Eeyore's balloon. He held it very tightly against himself, so that it shouldn't blow away, and he ran as fast as he could so as to get to Eeyore before Pooh did; for he thought that he would like to be the first one to give a present, just as if he had thought of it without being told by anybody.

- - - - - - - - - - - - -   - - - - - - - - - - - - -

- - - - - - - - - - - - -   - - - - - - - - - - - - -

Your present to baby

- -

Taking Steps

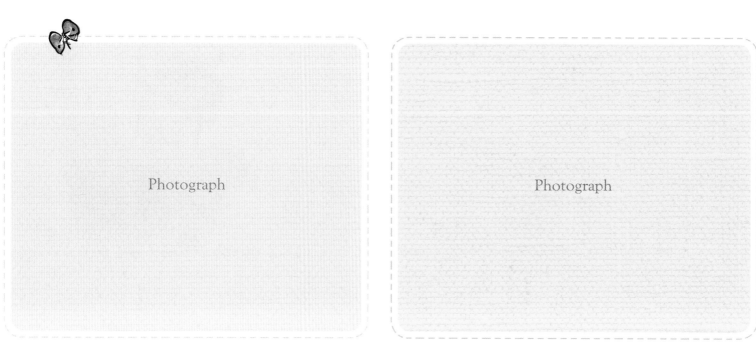

Photograph

Photograph

Crawling   Date _ _ _ _ _ _ _ _ _

Holding on   Date _ _ _ _ _ _ _ _ _

Photograph

Photograph

Standing up   Date _ _ _ _ _ _ _ _ _

First steps without help   Date _ _ _ _ _ _ _ _ _

First Words

First Sounds   Date   Favourite books

- - - - - - - - - - - - - - -   - - - - - - - -   - - - - - - - - - - - - - - -

- - - - - - - - - - - - - - -   - - - - - - - -   - - - - - - - - - - - - - - -

First Words   - - - - - - - - - - - - - - -

- - - - - - - - - - - - - - -   - - - - - - - -   - - - - - - - - - - - - - - -

- - - - - - - - - - - - - - -   - - - - - - - -   - - - - - - - - - - - - - - -

- - - - - - - - - - - - - - -   - - - - - - - -   - - - - - - - - - - - - - - -

- - - - - - - - - - - - - - -   - - - - - - - -   - - - - - - - - - - - - - - -

Binker's always talking, 'cos I'm teaching him to speak:
He sometimes likes to do it in a funny sort of squeak,
And he sometimes likes to do it in a hoodling sort of roar . . .
And I have to do it for him 'cos his throat is rather sore.

First Events

Focused eyes

- - - - - - - - - - - - - - - - - - -

Smiled

- - - - - - - - - - - - - - - - - - -

Sucked thumb or dummy

- - - - - - - - - - - - - - - - - - -

Slept through the night

- - - - - - - - - - - - - - - - - - -

Held head up

- - - - - - - - - - - - - - - - - - -

Played with hands

- - - - - - - - - - - - - - - - - - -

Played with feet

- - - - - - - - - - - - - - - - - - -

Clapped hands

- - - - - - - - - - - - - - - - - - -

Grasped an object

- - - - - - - - - - - - - - - - - - -

O Timothy Tim
Has ten pink toes,
And ten pink toes
Has Timothy Tim.
They go with him
Wherever he goes,
And wherever he goes
They go with him.

O Timothy Tim
Has two blue eyes,
And two blue eyes
Has Timothy Tim.
They cry with him
Whenever he cries,
And whenever he cries,
They cry with him.

Gurgled

- - - - - - - - - - - - - - - - - - -

Laughed

- - - - - - - - - - - - - - - - - - -

Said ma-ma

- - - - - - - - - - - - - - - - - - -

Said da-da

- - - - - - - - - - - - - - - - - - -

Spoke first words

- - - - - - - - - - - - - - - - - - -

Made animal noises

- - - - - - - - - - - - - - - - - - -

Rolled right over

- - - - - - - - - - - - - - - - - - -

Sat up

- - - - - - - - - - - - - - - - - - -

Started to crawl

Pulled him/herself upright

Stood alone

Took first steps with help

Took first steps alone

Started climbing

Wore shoes

Walked outside

Waved goodbye

Had a haircut

First baby-sitter

Recognised his/her name

Ate solid food

Drank from a cup

Used a spoon

Cut a tooth

First kiss

Favourite Things

Baby's favourite:

Games

_____

_____

_____

_____

Activities

_____

_____

Songs and nursery rhymes

_____

_____

Pictures

_____

_____

Toys

_____

_____

Books

_____

_____

Cuddly toys

_____

_____

People

_____

_____

_____

Animals

_____

_____

Sounds

_____

_____

Music

_____

_____

"What do you like doing best in the world, Pooh?"
"Well," said Pooh, "what I like best –" and then
he had to stop and think. Because although
Eating Honey was a very good thing to do, there
was a moment just before you began to eat it
which was better than when you were, but he
didn't know what it was called.

What makes baby laugh

_____

_____

_____

_____

45

Special Memories

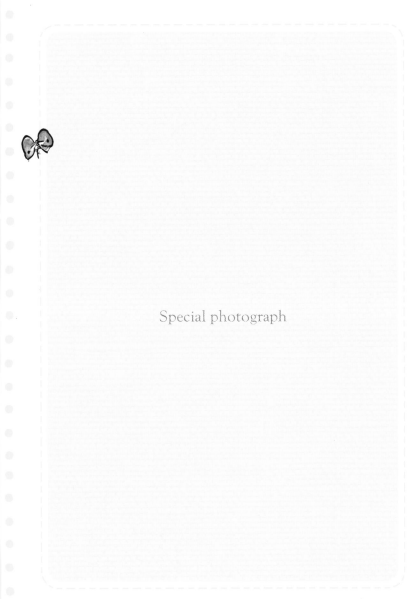

Special photograph

Date _ _ _ _ _ _ _ _ _ _ _ _ _ _ _

"Oh, Bear!" said Christopher Robin.
"How I do love you!"
"So do I," said Pooh.

Looking back on the first year of your baby's life you may like to record some special moments.

First friends

_ _

_ _

_ _

_ _

Special things to remember

_ _

_ _

_ _

_ _

Funny ways

_____

_____

_____

_____

_____

Photograph

Baby's friends

The Future

Plans for the future

_____

_____

_____

"Do you know what A means, little Piglet?"
"No, Eeyore, I don't."
"It means Learning, it means Education, it
means all the things that you and Pooh
haven't got. That's what A means."
"Oh," said Piglet again. "I mean, does it?"
he explained very quickly.

Possible nursery schools

_____

_____

_____

Baby's character

_____

_____

_____

_____

Scrapbook

What's become of John boy?
    Nothing at all,
He played with his skipping rope,
    He played with his ball.
He ran after butterflies,
    Blue ones and red;
He did a hundred happy things –
    And then went to bed.

Scrapbook

When I was One,
I had just begun.

When I was Two,
I was nearly new.

When I was Three,
I was hardly Me.

When I was Four
I was not much more.

When I was Five,
I was just alive.

But now I am Six, I'm as clever as clever.
So I think I'll be six now for ever and ever.